Bella's Chinese New Year

Written by Stacey Zolt Hara

Illustrated by Steve Pileggi

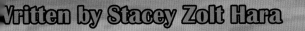

"To the real Bella, who has enchanted me across four continents." – SZH

For information, address Travel with Bella via email at info@travelwithbella.com.
www.travelwithbella.com

Composed in Singapore
Illustrated in the United States of America
Printed in Malaysia
First impression 2011
ISBN: 978-981-08-8127-6

"Bella! Hurry up or we'll miss the party. C'mon!"

I hear Mommy at the front door as I check myself out in her bedroom mirror, admiring my fancy qipao for the Chinese New Year party at school today. It's a soft, silky red dress embroidered with pink flowers.

In Singapore, where I live with my family, the streets are lined with red lanterns and cherry blossoms for the festive season. Shiny red door decorations welcome visitors to homes and shops.

The city sparkles with festive energy for the New Year celebration. Singapore is a long way from Chicago, where I was born, but for me it is home.

Every morning I ride the bus to school with Mommy. I say hello to Peter, the bus driver, and I put a gold Singapore dollar coin in the slot. The machine spits out a ticket that I love to hold while we ride.

I wave good bye to Daddy as the bus pulls away. There are so many different people on the bus – all riding together past the pastel-colored shophouses to begin the day.

Two teenage girls in school uniforms whisper gossip to each other as they sit on the bench. An old man closes his eyes as the bus bumps along, catching a quick snooze on his way to work.

Mrs. Tan boards at the next stop. "Nihao Bella," she says, pinching my cheek as she walks to her usual seat.

In Singapore, people speak English and Mandarin. My laoshi, teacher, teaches me Mandarin at school.

"Nihao," I say and wave. Mrs. Tan always giggles at my curly hair, because everyone's hair here is straight.

She sometimes offers me candy, and, sometimes, my mommy lets me eat it.

"Xie xie," I say back, thanking her for the yummy treat.

When I arrive at my cozy school house, I gasp at the decorations – it's a real party! My teachers are all wearing fancy qipaos instead of their usual blue jeans. They look so beautiful.

I've brought two oranges to exchange with my friends at school. When I give my friends the oranges, that means I'm wishing them good luck and wealth for the New Year.

"Xie xie Bella," says my friend Gracie as she hands me two oranges in exchange to bring my family good luck and wealth too!

"Gong Xi Fa Cai!" I tell Gracie, which means "Happy Chinese New Year!"

At the party, Gracie and I sit with our friends Nura and Parita. Red paper lanterns sway in the wind above our picnic table as we nibble pineapple tarts.

Gracie is Chinese, Nura is Malay and Parita is Indian. All of them are Singaporean, and I am American.

But today, we are all celebrating Chinese New Year together in Singapore – a place where many people from many different places all over the world come to live and play.

Laoshi helps us make a lo hei salad to make our New Year wishes, a traditional treat Singaporeans only eat during the Chinese New Year holiday.

We toss together peanuts, salmon, carrots, radishes, cinnamon, pomelo, sesame seeds and crunchy crisps in the shape of golden pillows. We squeeze the salad with our chopsticks and toss the food as high in the air as we can – seven times in all for health and good luck in the New Year.

Gracie and Nura fling the salad so high the food gets all over their hair. What fun to play with our food without getting into trouble from Laoshi!

As we settle in to eat our lo hei salad, Laoshi gives us each a small red envelope called a hong bao.
All over the world, Chinese children get these special envelopes from their families on Chinese New Year.
I'm so lucky to get hong bao too while I celebrate Chinese New Year in Singapore.

"Let's open them together!" I tell my friends.

We each open our shiny envelopes with the Chinese characters and find $2 bills inside!
We can't believe it – what a fabulous start to a lucky New Year.

"Gong Xi Fa Cai!" we all sing together as we giggle and hold hands.

Mandarin Glossary and Pronunciation Guide

NI HAO – "knee how" – Hello. If you add 'ma' to the end, it means "how are you doing today?"

QIPAO – "chee-pow" – Traditional Shanghainese dress for women, usually made from silk

XIE XIE – "shay shay" – Thank you

LAOSHI – "l'ow sure" (ow as in ouch!) – Teacher

GONG XI FA CAI – "gong shee fa s'eye" – Happy New Year

HONG BAO – "hong bow" (as in take a bow) – Red envelopes containing money passed from adults to children

LO HEI – "low hey" – A Prosperity Toss salad consumed during Chinese New Year. In Cantonese, it literally means "tossing luck"

For fun activities to celebrate Chinese New Year Bella-style, go to www.travelwithbella.com.

Bella's Chinese New Year Curriculum Guide

Facilitating activities around Chinese New Year is a great way to expose children to Chinese culture. These crafts projects and games will deepen the learning experience while reading Bella's Chinese New Year at home or in the classroom.

BUILD A ZODIAC

Prior to reading Bella's Chinese New Year, discuss with children the convept of the Chinese zodiac calendar, explaining that Chinese people all over the world celebrate a different New Year than the calendar year of January-December. Theirs is based on the zodiac calendar. Depending on one's birth year, he or she is a particular animal and is said to take on that animal's traits.

See the chart on the next page for the animals and corresponding years.

The kids can build a wheel with each zodiac animal, then discover which they are. Ask the kids: Do they think they are like that animal, why or why not? What about their parents, siblings, grandparents or teacher? Which animal are they?

Put a photographs on the wheel or draw the faces of the child's various family members underneath their respective zodiac signs.

WHAT ANIMAL AM I?

Using the zodiac chart opposite for reference, explain to the child which animal they are according to the Chinese zodiac calendar. Then, paste a picture of each child's face onto a plain piece of paper, leaving plenty of white space around the photo.
Lay out raw materials like construction paper, felt, string, paint and markers for the kids to use.

Each child can then use the raw materials to transform their photo into their zodiac animal, literally becoming thier zodiac sign. For example, a "tiger" might paint an orange body, ears and fur, then use black felt or string to create stripes.

This is a great way to explain that the Chinese believe each person born in a particular year takes on the characteristics of the animal for that year. Forever in their lives, that animal is a part of them.

Chinese Zodiac Signs and Yearly Calendar

Rabbit
1927 1939 1951 1963 1975 1987 1999 2011

Dragon
1928 1940 1952 1964 1976 1988 2000 2012

Snake
1929 1941 1953 1965 1977 1989 2001 2013

Horse
1930 1942 1954 1966 1978 1990 2002 2014

Sheep
1931 1943 1955 1967 1979 1991 2003 2015

Monkey
1932 1944 1956 1968 1980 1992 2004 2016

Rooster
1933 1945 1957 1969 1981 1993 2005 2017

Dog
1934 1946 1958 1970 1982 1994 2006 2018

Pig
1935 1947 1959 1971 1983 1995 2007 2019

Rat
1924 1936 1948 1960 1972 1984 1996 2008

Ox
1925 1937 1949 1961 1973 1985 1997 2009

Tiger
1926 1938 1950 1962 1974 1986 1998 2010

MAKE A RED LANTERN

Building a red paper lantern is a fun way to replicate the festive scenes in Bella's Chinese New Year in your classroom or at home.

Shape each of four long pipe cleaners into circles then secure them together at the top with a twist tie. Fan the pipe cleaner circles out to form a globe shape, then secure them at the bottom with 2-3 twist ties so the wires retain their shape.

With red tissue paper, wrape the wire globe and glue the loose bits down like you're wrapping a present. Be sure to leave openings at the top and bottom.

At the bottom of the lantern, tie several pieces of yellow yarn to simulate the fringes on traditional lanterns. At the top, tie a long loop of yellow string . Reshape a paper clip to act as a hook. Loop one end through the top lantern string and use the other to hang the lantern in your doorway.

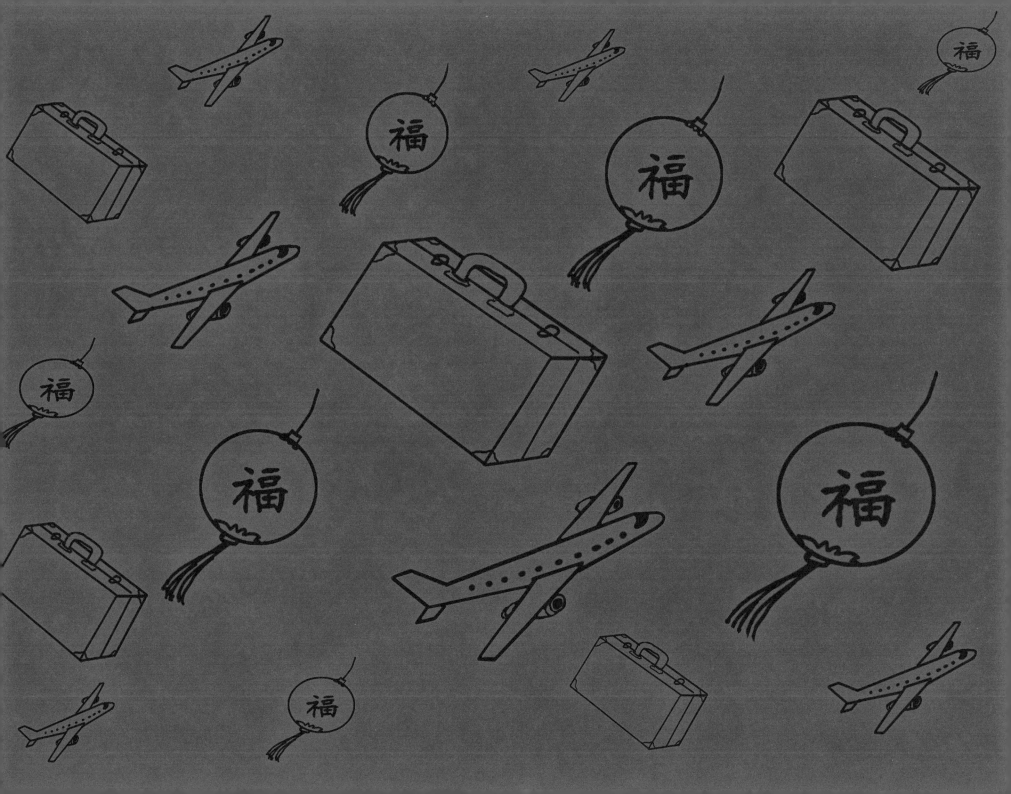